The Organist's
Treasury
Book Two

The Organist's Treasury
Book Two

One Hundred Pieces for Manuals

Kevin Mayhew

We hope you enjoy *The Organist's Treasury Book 2*.
Further copies are available from your local music shop
or Christian bookshop.

In case of difficulty, please contact the publisher direct by writing to:

The Sales Department
KEVIN MAYHEW LTD
Rattlesden
Bury St Edmunds
Suffolk IP30 0SZ

Phone 0449 737978
Fax 0449 737834

Please ask for our complete catalogue of outstanding Church Music.

First published in Great Britain in 1993 by Kevin Mayhew Ltd

© Copyright 1993 Kevin Mayhew Ltd

ISBN 0 86209 376 7

All or part of these pieces have been edited and/or arranged by
Joanne Clarke, Colin Hand, Alan Ridout, Anthea Smith and
Christopher Tambling and are the copyright of Kevin Mayhew Ltd.

Front Cover: *Angel Musician* by Melozzo da Forli (1438-1494).
Vatican Museums and Galleries, Rome/Bridgeman Art Library, London.
Reproduced by kind permission.

Picture Research: Jane Rayson
Cover design by Juliette Clarke and Graham Johnstone

Printed and bound in Great Britain.

Contents

Foreword

All one hundred pieces in this collection of music from the seventeenth to the twentieth century may be played on the manuals. *The Organist's Treasury* is offered as a treasure chest of useful music both to the organist who is at home with the pedals but does not feel the urge to use them all the time, and to the pianist-turned-organist who feels more comfortable using the manuals only.

Many of the pieces appear in their original form; others were originally conceived for the pedals and have required judicious re-arrangement for the present book. A third group of pieces has been adapted from the extensive piano repertoire to make a pleasing and suitable contribution.

In keeping with modern editorial practice, the text of *The Organist's Treasury* is generally uncluttered with manual and registration suggestions. This approach enables the notes to speak for themselves and allows the performer to make his or her own choice in these matters. It also makes the actual process of reading the music easier.

We hope that many organists will gain much pleasure from these pieces: we have certainly enjoyed choosing them.

THE PUBLISHER

MINUET

Joseph Haydn (1732-1809)

EVENTIDE

Heinrich Hofmann (1842-1902)

GLORIA

Jean Titelouze (1563-1633)

15

To Sophie, Bianca and Tom

FESTIVAL MARCH

Philip Moore (b. 1943)

RECESSIONAL

César Franck (1822-1890)

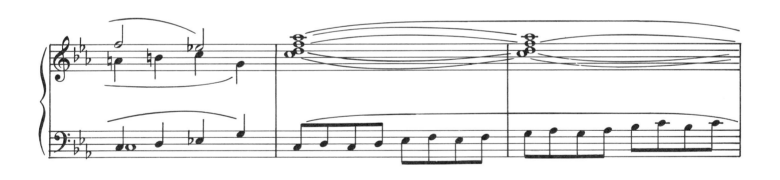

SLOW AIR

Samuel Wesley (1766-1837)

FESTIVAL
Carl Nielsen (1865-1931)

For Dom Paul Eggleston

ANDANTE TRANQUILLO

Dom Andrew Moore (b. 1954)

2½ minutes

24

Fine

D.C. al Fine

RONDEAU

Jean-Philippe Rameau (1683-1764)

D.C. al Fine

BENEDICTION

June Nixon

29

PRIÈRE

César Franck (1822-1890)

A.M.M.

ROMANZA

Philip Marshall (b. 1921)

PRAYER

Alfred Hollins (1865-1942)

PRELUDE IN B♭

Johann Rinck (1770-1846)

AVE VERUM CORPUS

Wolfgang Amadeus Mozart (1756-1791)

ANDANTE TRANQUILLO

Dom Gregory Murray (1905-1992)

41

MAESTOSO

César Franck (1822-1890)

43

MINUET AND TRIO from Sonata No. 15

Joseph Haydn (1732-1809)

Fine

D.C. al Fine
senza ripet.

45

FESTIVAL FINALE

Malcolm Archer (b. 1952)

poco rall.   *a tempo*

rall.

FIRST LOSS

Robert Schumann (1810-1856)

CONCLUDING VOLUNTARY

Thomas Walmisley (1814-1856)

MARCH

Peter Ilyich Tchaikovsky (1840-1893)

Sr. M 5-5-96

ÉLÉGIE

César Franck (1822-1890)

For Elgar Lumsdon
CAVATINA
Richard Lloyd (b. 1933)

Andante, senza rigore

55

56

57

PRELUDE IN E MINOR

Alexander Scriabin (1872-1915)

Sr.M- 24-9-95

PRELUDE IN G MINOR

Johann Rinck (1770-1846)

For Ken

ROYAL KNIGHTS: A Ceremonial March

Christopher Tambling (b. 1964)

EPITAPH

Alan Ridout (b. 1934)

COUNTRY DANCE

James Hook (1746-1827)

66

PRELUDE IN C MINOR

Henryk Pachulski (1859-1921)

OFFERTOIRE

César Franck (1822-1890)

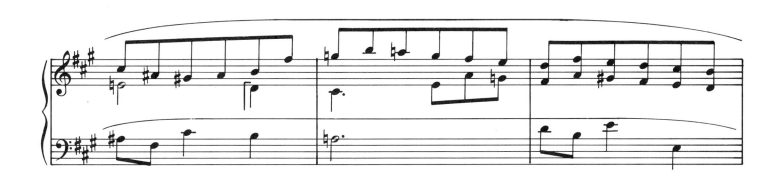

rall.

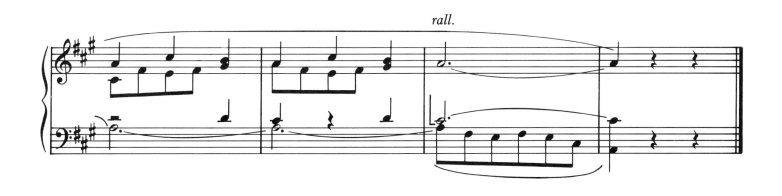

WHY?

Vladimir Rebikov (1866-1920)

MUSING

John Jordan (b. 1941)

More cheerful (*the same speed*)

slow down to the end

75

DOMINE, EXAUDI

Stanley Vann (b. 1910)

78

ALBUM LEAF

Robert Schumann (1810-1856)

THEME FROM 'JUPITER'

Gustav Holst (1874-1934)

81

LA FURSTEMBERG

Michel Corrette (1709-1795)

MELODY

Charles Stokes (1784-1839)

Sr. M   5-5-96

MEMORIES OF CHILDHOOD

Enrique Granados (1867-1916)

For Christina Bourne

PREAMBLE

Richard Lloyd (b. 1933)

For Sheila

COUNTRY MINUET

Graham Knott (b. 1934)

PRELUDE IN C

Johann Rinck (1770-1846)

For Catherine, Tom and Carys

IN PASTURES GREEN

Paul Bryan (b. 1950)

95

NEW YEAR'S SONG

Robert Schumann (1810-1856)

Sr.M - 20-8-95

For Dom Cyprian Stockford

NOBILMENTE

Dom Andrew Moore (b. 1954)

TARANTELLA

Moritz Moszkowski (1854-1925)

TO A WILD ROSE

Edward MacDowell (1860-1908)

PEACEFUL MEDITATION

Colin Mawby (b. 1936)

108

FUGUE

Georg Philipp Telemann (1681-1767)

TOCCATA

Domenico Paradies (1707-1791)

BERCEUSE

Philip Moore (b. 1943)

119

ALLEGRO

César Franck (1822-1890)

121

CANZONA

Dom Gregory Murray (1905-1992)

PANIS ANGELICUS

César Franck (1822-1890)

POSTLUDIUM

Franz Liszt (1811-1886)

127

ANDANTE CON MOTO

Felix Mendelssohn (1809-1847)

Sr.M   29-6-97

For the Revd Francis Woolley

FESTIVE PROCESSION

Paul Bryan (b. 1950)

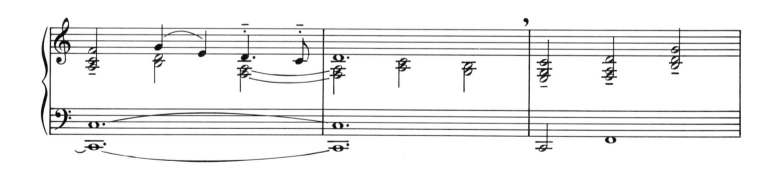

* These bottom C's may be played by the pedal if preferred.

Sw. reed

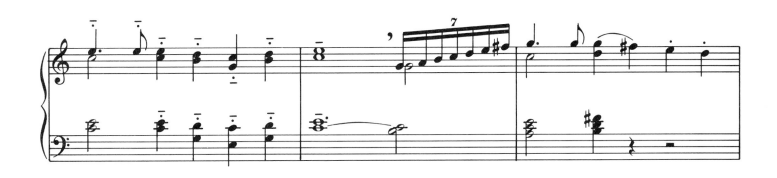

OVER THE PAGE

WHERE ONLY THE LORD GIVES GUIDANCE

Johann Töpfer (1791-1870)

135

REFLECTION

Enrique Granados (1867-1916)

Lento con tenerezza

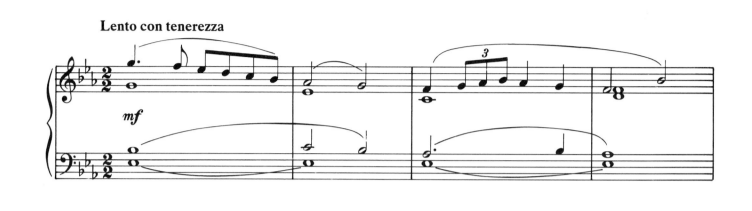

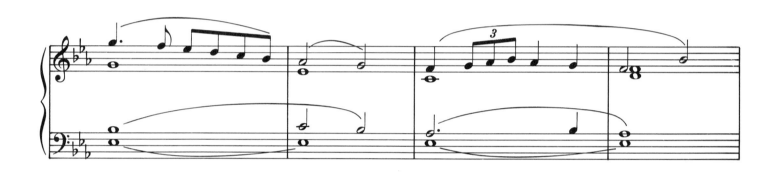

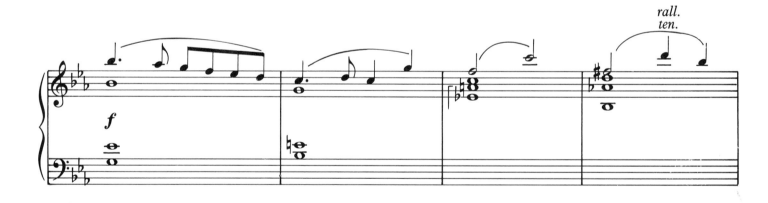

PRELUDE IN D MINOR

Anton Bruckner (1824-1896)

Andante

MEDITATION

Norman Warren (b. 1934)

IDYLL

Edward MacDowell (1860-1908)

For Dr John Richardson

NOCTURNE

Richard Lloyd (b. 1933)

EVENING

Alfred Hollins (1865-1942)

147

MELBOURNE MARCH

June Nixon

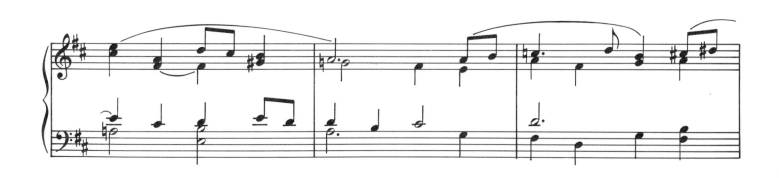

151

ANDANTINO

César Franck (1822-1890)

ADAGIO

Christopher Tambling (b. 1964)

PASTORALE

William Russell (1777-1813)

AVE VERUM CORPUS

Stanley Vann (b. 1910)

159

ANDANTE

Johann Rinck (1770-1846)

For Nick Smith

A TRUMPET GAVOTTE

Christopher Tambling (b. 1964)

EVA AND WALTER

Enrique Granados (1867-1916)

MELODIE

Theodor Kirchner (1823-1903)

Con moto (♩=120)

CALM REFLECTION

Colin Mawby (b. 1936)

PRELUDE ON A BASQUE NOËL

César Franck (1822-1890)

171

AN EVENING LITANY

Malcolm Archer (b. 1952)

THE ROSE GARDEN

Edward MacDowell (1860-1908)

QUESTION AND ANSWER

Max Reger (1873-1916)

GRAVE

Peter Ilyich Tchaikovsky (1840-1893)

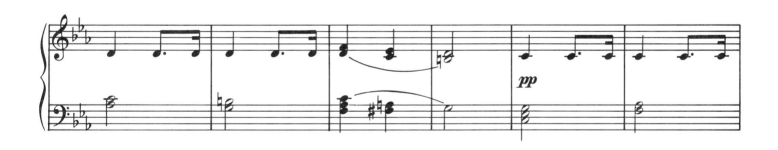

A PEACEFUL PASTORALE

Stanley Vann (b. 1910)

Sr. M - 4 - 6 - 95

CEBELL

Henry Purcell (1659-1695)

For Ken Murray

INTERLUDE

Christopher Tambling (b. 1964)

184

AIR and GAVOTTE

John Sanders (b. 1933)

Tempo di gavotta (♩=c.60)

188

189

IMPROMPTU

Moritz Moszkowski (1854-1925)

SARABANDE

Johann Fischer (c.1670-1746)

ALLEGRETTO

César Franck (1822-1890)

ARIA

Noel Rawsthorne (b. 1929)

ALLEGRO NON TROPPO

Felix Mendelssohn (1809-1847)

MINUET

Henry Purcell (1659-1695)

200

COMMUNION

Malcolm Archer (b. 1952)

LIED

Heinrich Hofmann (1842-1902)

VOLUNTARY

William Croft (1678-1727)

Sr. M- 4-6-95

O FOR THE WINGS OF A DOVE

Felix Mendelssohn (1809-1847)

GOD WHO MADEST EARTH AND HEAVEN

Sigfrid Karg-Elert (1877-1933)

211

Sk.M   28-4-96

AN OLD MAN'S TALE

Enrique Granados (1867-1916)

213

PETITE PIÈCE

César Franck (1822-1890)

INTERLUDE

Noel Rawsthorne (b. 1929)

For Ian Shaw

RECOLLECTION

Richard Lloyd (b. 1933)

VALSE

Génari Karganov (1858-1890)

GAVOTTE

Louis Daquin (1694-1772)